We Are Friends:

Stories from Frog Song Farm Sanctuary

frogsongfarmsanctuary.org

KDP ISBN 9781082058141

If differences don't matter to them,
then why should they matter to us?

In loving memory of Lula and Tommy

The Donkeys Gladys and June

Welcome to Frog Song Farm Sanctuary where we all get along. Turn the pages to see!

Lucy, the cat, says, "Penny, you have a big head."

Penny, the horse, says, "Lucy, you have a small head."

We are different but we are friends.

Lucky, the goat, says, "Frannie, you are up."

Frannie, the dog, says, "Lucky, you are down."

We are different but we are friends.

Clyde, the goat, says, "I am holding my head up high."

Tommy, the llama, says, "I am holding my head up higher."

We are different but we are friends.

Tulip, the goat, says, "I like eating hay in the sunshine."

Savi, the cow, says, "I like eating hay in the sunshine too."

We are different but we are friends.

Clyde, the goat, says, "Totes, you are a tall goat."

Totes, the goat, says, "Clyde, you are a short goat."

We are different but we are friends.

Rudy, the donkey, says, "I am white."

Andy, the donkey, says, "I am brown."

We are different but we are friends.

Tommy, the llama, says, "I have a long neck."

Sam, the donkey, says, "I have a short neck."

We are different but we are friends.

Oreo, the pony, says, "Johanna, you are one color."

Johanna, the goat, says, "Oreo, you are two colors."

We are different but we are friends.

Happy, the goat, says, "I am on the floor."

Lula and Frannie, the dogs, say, "We are on the seats."

We are different but we are friends.

Lula, the dog, says, "Maggie, you have a wide tail."

Maggie, the horse, says, "Lula, you have a narrow tail."

We are different but we are friends.

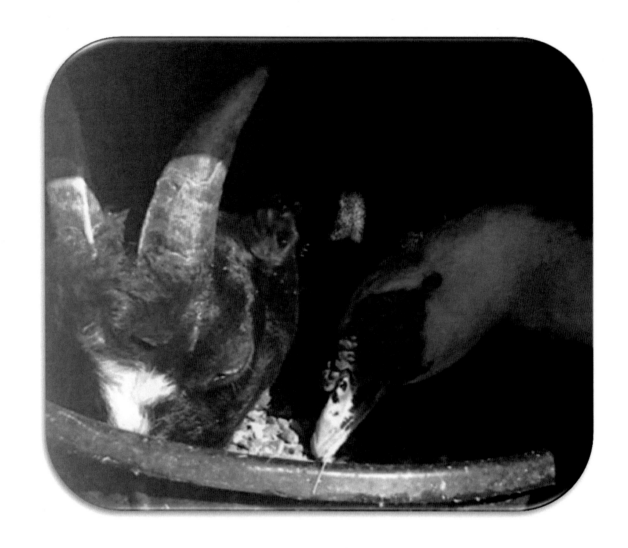

Happy, the goat, says, "Willy, you eat slowly."

Willy, the duck, says, "Happy, you eat quickly."

We are different but we are friends.

Swashi, the goat, says, "I am inside the hay shed."

Honey Bun, the goat, says, "I am outside the hay shed."

We are different but we are friends.

Ethel, the cat, says, "Savi, you have a cool nose."

Savi, the cow, says, "Ethel, you have a warm nose."

We are different but we are friends.

Harry, the dog, says, "Willy, you have webbed feet."

Willy, the duck, says, "Harry, you have furry feet."

We are different but we are friends.

Happy, the goat, says, "William, please pet me."

Sam, the donkey, says, "Thanks, William, for petting me first."

We are different but we are friends.

Lily, the calf, says, "Lula, you have short legs."

Lula, the dog, says, "Lily, you have long legs."

We are different but we are friends.

Gladys, the donkey, says, "I like to eat hay in the morning."

Swashi, the goat, says, "I like to eat hay all day."

We are different but we are friends.

Happy, the goat, says, "I like Lindsey. She is my friend."

Lindsey, the girl, says, "I like Happy. He is my friend."

We are different but we are friends.

Ethel, the cat, says, "Tommy, you are tall."

Tommy, the llama, says, "Ethel you are short."

We are different but we are friends.

Bob, the goat, says, "Roy, you are large."

Georgie, the cat, says, "Bob, you are medium."

Roy, the donkey, says, "Georgie, you are small."

We are different but we are friends.

Lucky, the goat, says, "Willy, you are round."

Willy, the duck says, "Lucky, you are rounder than me."

We are different but we are friends.

Elvis, the cow, says, "I am the biggest."

Elliot, the cow, says, "I am getting bigger."

Little Bit, the cow, says, "I will be big someday."

We are different but we are friends.

Dae, the goat, says, "I have white fur with a little black."

Drogo, the goat, says, "I have black fur with a little white."

We are different but we are friends.

Sam, the baby donkey, says, "I was born here. I like it here."

Lula, the dog, says, "I was adopted. I like it here too."

We are different but we are friends.

Happy, the goat, says, "I am happy at Frog Song Farm Sanctuary."

Renny, the horse, says, "I am happy you are happy, Happy. I am happy at Frog Song Farm Sanctuary too, where we all get along."

Thank you for reading our book.

Author VieVie Baird with Totes the Goat

VieVie spent thirty-eight years as an educator. She started her career as an elementary teacher and retired as a Science Specialist for the Florida Department of Education. She spends her time reading, volunteering, and playing with her two feisty dogs. As a breast cancer survivor she calls Frog Song Farm Sanctuary one of her recovery "Happy Places."

For more about Frog Song Farm Sanctuary, visit our website at FrogSongFarmSanctuary.org. See us also on Instagram or Facebook at Frog Song Farm Sanctuary

Photographer Kay Williams with Her Husband Richard and the Dogs

Kathryn (Kay) Weymouth Williams and her husband, Richard D'Antoni moved to Cairo, Georgia in the Spring of 2016 in order to fulfill Kay's dream of having an animal sanctuary. Together, they started Frog Song Farm Sanctuary, a 501c3 charitable organization that currently is home to donkeys, horses, cows, goats, ducks, cats and some very spoiled dogs.

Made in the USA
Columbia, SC
04 August 2019